Singapore Math®
Tests

3A

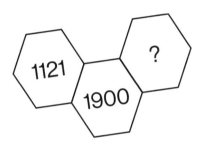

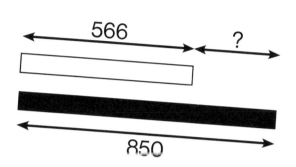

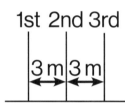

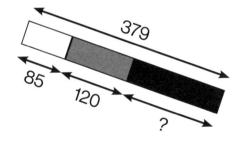

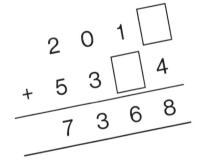

Differentiated Unit Tests
Continual Assessments

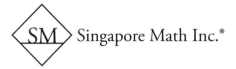

Singapore Math Inc.®

BLANK

Preface

Singapore Math® Tests is a series of structured assessments to help teachers evaluate student progress. The tests align with the content of Primary Mathematics Common Core textbooks.

Each level offers differentiated tests (Test A and Test B) to suit individual needs. Tests consist of multiple-choice questions that assess comprehension of key concepts and free response questions that demonstrate problem solving skills. Three continual assessments cover topics from earlier units and a year-end assessment covers the entire curriculum.

Test A focuses on key concepts and fundamental problem solving skills.

Test B focuses on the application of analytical skills, thinking skills, and heuristics.

Contents

BLANK

Name: _____   Date: _____

Test A

30 min

30

Score

Unit 1 Numbers to 10,000

Section A (2 points each)
Circle the correct option: **A**, **B**, **C**, or **D**.

1. Which of the following is the same as five thousand, fifty-five?

   A ⟨5,000⟩   **B** ⟨5,005⟩

   C ⟨5,055⟩   **D** ⟨5,505⟩

2. Which digit is in the thousands place?

   A 1   **B** 8

   C 6   **D** 4

Tests 3A

3. What is the value of the digit '9' in this number?

3,970

A 9   **B** 90

C 900   **D** 9,000

4. Which set of numbers is arranged in order from greatest to smallest?

A 2,013 ✦ 2,301 ✦ 1,230

B 1,230 ✦ 2,013 ✦ 2,301

C 3,012 ✦ 2,013 ✦ 2,301

D 3,012 ✦ 2,301 ✦ 2,013

5. What is the value of the missing number?

6,000 + ☐ ? + 6 = 6,066

A 6 ones   **B** 6 tens

C 60 tens   **D** 600 ones

Section B (2 points each)

6. Write the number.

a) four thousand, two hundred nine

b) eight thousand, eighty-eight

7. Write the number in words.

a)

b)

8. In 3,208,

   a) the digit 3 is in the _____ place.

   b) the value of the digit 2 is _____.

9. What number is 1 less than 2,100?

   ┌──────────────────────────┐
   │   │
   │   │
   │   │
   └──────────────────────────┘

10. What number is 1 more than 8,709?

   ┌──────────────────────────┐
   │   │
   │   │
   │   │
   └──────────────────────────┘

11. Which of the following numbers is greater than 5,138?

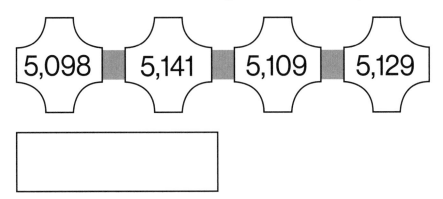

12. Which of the following numbers has 6 in its hundreds place?

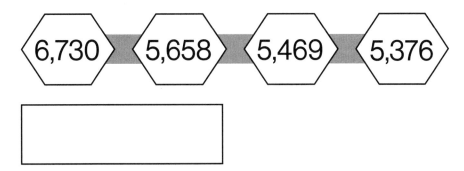

13. Write the missing numbers.

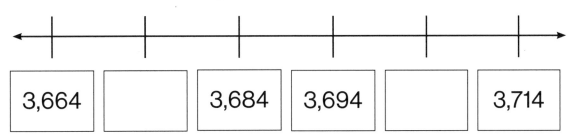

14. Look at the number pattern.
    Write the missing numbers.

| | 5,371 | 5,271 | 5,171 | | 4,971 |

15. Round 4,598

    a)   to the nearest ten: _____

    b)   to the nearest thousand: _____

Name: _____ Date: _____

Test B

30 min

30
Score

Unit 1 Numbers to 10,000

Section A (2 points each)
Circle the correct option: **A**, **B**, **C**, or **D**.

1. Which of the following numbers has the same value as 51 hundreds and 7 ones?

   A (517)   **B** (5,017)

   C (5,107)   **D** (5,170)

2. In which of the following numbers does the digit 6 have the smallest value?

   A (8,602)   **B** (8,026)

   C (2,860)   **D** (6,028)

3. Which of the following has the greatest value?

    A 3,000 + 900 + 9

    B 2,000 + 900 + 90 + 9

    C 3,000 + 90 + 9

    D 3,000 + 900 + 90

4. Look at the pattern. What is the missing number?

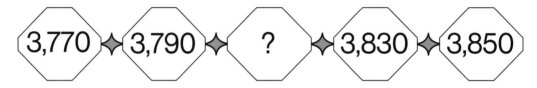

    A 3,730   **B** 3,800

    C 3,810   **D** 3,820

5. Read the clues. What is the number X?

    X is greater than 3,000 but smaller than 6,000.
    The digits in the tens and hundreds places are 0.
    The sum of all its digits is 8.

    A 2,060   **B** 4,002

    C 4,040   **D** 5,003

Section B (2 points each)

6. Arrange the numbers in order.
   Begin with the smallest.

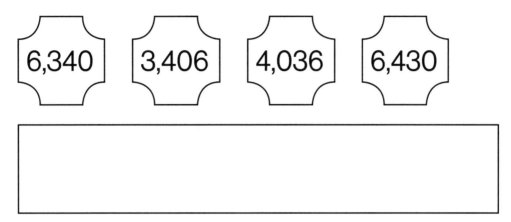

7.  stands for a number.

   It is 100 less than 2,099.

   What number does 🎄 stand for?

8. What is the missing number?

   7,040 is _____ tens more than 7,000.

9. I am a 4-digit number.
The digit in the hundreds place is 5 less than the ones place.
The digit in the tens place is 5 more than the thousands place.
Which of the following numbers am I?

6,813   1,863   6,318   1,368

```
┌────────────────────┐
│                    │
│                    │
│                    │
└────────────────────┘
```

10. What is the greatest 4-digit odd number that can be formed using each of the digits below only once?

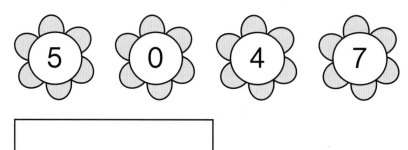

5   0   4   7

```
┌────────────────────┐
│                    │
│                    │
└────────────────────┘
```

11. Wanda is thinking of a 4-digit number.

The number is between 2,000 and 3,000.
The digit in the tens place is 3 more than 6.
The digit in the ones place is 4 less than 9.
The digit in the hundreds place is 0.

What number is it?

12. Which two add up to 10,000?

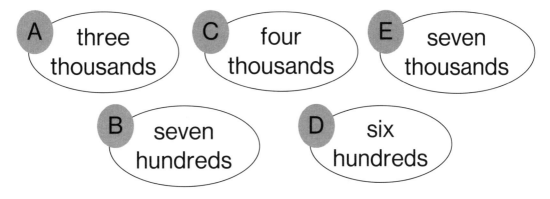

A three thousands

C four thousands

E seven thousands

B seven hundreds

D six hundreds

13. Look at the pattern.
    Write the missing number.

1,620   1,740   1,860   [ ]   2,100

14. Circle true or false.

    $9,867 < 600 + 7 + 9,000 + 80$

    TRUE   FALSE

15. Round 850

    a)   to the nearest thousand:

    b)   to the nearest hundred:

Name: _____ Date: _____

Test A

45 min

50

Score

Unit 2 Addition and Subtraction

Section A (2 points each)

Circle the correct option: **A**, **B**, **C**, or **D**.

1. What is the sum of these two numbers?

A 8,880   **B** 8,800

C 8,280   **D** 8,080

2. Subtract 340 from 2,973.
    What is the answer?

```
   2 9 7 3
 -   3 4 0
 _____

 _____
```

A 2,673   **B** 2,633

C 3,313   **D** 3,373

3. Find the sum of 432 and 1,217.
   In the answer, what digit is in the hundreds place?

   A 1   **B** 6

   C 5   **D** 4

4. Which of the following gives a different answer from
   the others?

   A 234 + 345   **B** 2,599 − 1,020

   C 1,889 − 310   **D** 1,070 + 509

5. What are the missing digits?

$$\begin{array}{r} \boxed{?}\,9\;2\;8 \\ -\;4\;6\;\boxed{?}\;7 \\ \hline 3\;3\;2\;1 \\ \hline \end{array}$$

   A 7 and 4   **B** 1 and 0

   C 7 and 0   **D** 1 and 4

Section B (2 points each)

6. What is the sum of 3,122 and 1,434?

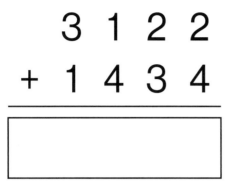

```
  3 1 2 2
+ 1 4 3 4
```

7. Subtract 62 tens from 2,789.
   What is the answer?

8. Write the missing digits.

```
  2 0 1 ☐
+ 5 3 ☐ 4
  7 3 6 8
```

9. Write the missing digits.

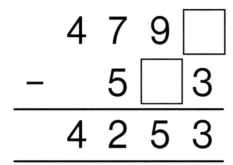

$$
\begin{array}{r}
4\ 7\ 9\ \square \\
-\quad\quad 5\ \square\ 3 \\
\hline
4\ 2\ 5\ 3 \\
\hline
\end{array}
$$

10.

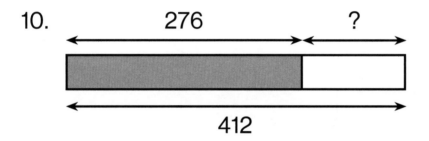

The value of the missing part is _____.

11.

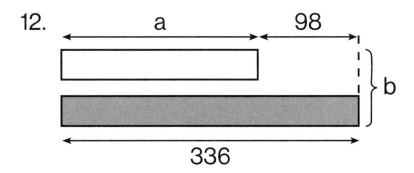

The difference between the two bars is _____.

12.

a) The value of the shorter bar is _____.

b) The total of the two bars is _____.

13. Fiona has 1,466 stickers in her collection. Her brother gives her another 230 stickers. How many stickers does she have in her collection now?

14. Factory A produced 5,775 skateboards in a day. This was 430 more than Factory B produced in a day. How many skateboards did Factory B produce in a day?

15. Ahmad made 4,138 meatballs on Saturday. After he sold some meatballs, 1,230 meatballs were left.
How many meatballs did he sell?

Section C (4 points each)

16. Polina collected 1,964 cards.
    David collected 350 fewer cards than Polina.

    a)   How many cards did David collect?

    He collected _____ cards.

    b)   How many cards did both of them collect?

    Both of them collected _____ cards
    together.

17. There are 4,080 fiction books in a library.
There are 1,122 more non-fiction books than fiction books in the library.
How many books are there altogether in the library?

There are _____ books altogether in the library.

18. The difference between two numbers is 1,700.
The smaller number is 530.
What is the sum of the two numbers?

The sum of the two numbers is _____.

19. In a project, Allison, Brian and Connie collected 1,045 used books altogether.
Allison collected 457 used books.
She collected 120 more books than Brian.
How many used books did Connie collect?

Connie collected _____ used books.

20.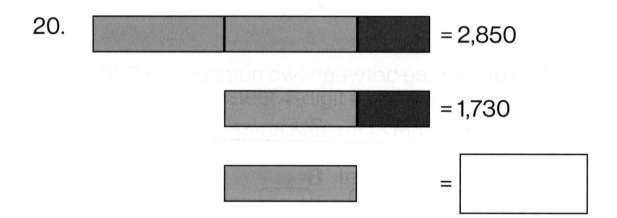

= 2,850

= 1,730

=

Name: _____   Date: _____

Test B   45 min

	50

Score

Unit 2 Addition and Subtraction

Section A (2 points each)
Circle the correct option: **A**, **B**, **C**, or **D**.

1. Look at the pattern.
    What is the missing number?

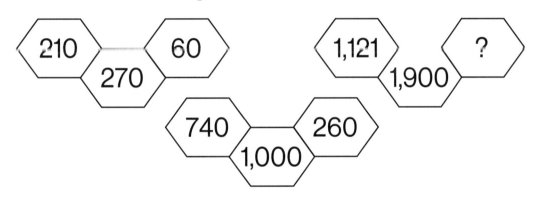

A 3,021	**B** 1,658
C 779	**D** 342

2. What is the missing number?
    $\boxed{?} - 2{,}938 = 4{,}438$

A 7,376	**B** 7,366
C 6,376	**D** 6,366

3. The table below shows the number of students who signed up for the various activities at Field Day.

Activity	Number of Participants
Basketball	289
Relay Race	735
Soccer	234

How many students signed up for Field Day altogether?

A 1,248

B 1,024

C 1,148

D 1,258

4. José brought 6,259 bottles of water to sell at the fair. At the end of the day, he had 2,143 bottles left. How many bottles of water did he sell?

A 8,402

B 8,316

C 4,116

D 4,152

5. When these numbers are added up, what digit is in the ones place of the sum?

$1 + 2 + 3 + 4 + 5 + 6 + 7 + 8 + 9 + 10$

A 1　　　　　　　**B** 2

C 0　　　　　　　**D** 5

Section B (2 points each)

6. In 4,070, what is the difference between the values of the digit 4 and the digit 7?

7. What is the missing number?

5,470 − 2,398 = [   ] + 70 + 2

8. Look at the pattern and fill in the missing numbers.

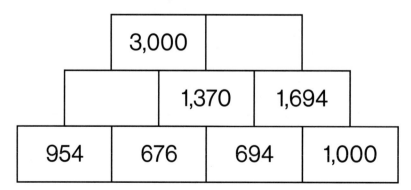

9. Write the missing digits.

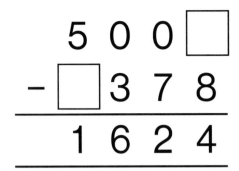

$$\begin{array}{r} 5\ 0\ 0\ \square \\ -\ \square\ 3\ 7\ 8 \\ \hline 1\ 6\ 2\ 4 \end{array}$$

10. Fill in the boxes with 6, 7, 8 and 9.
Use each number only once.

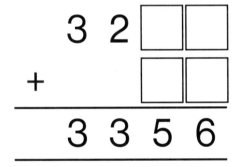

$$\begin{array}{r} 3\ 2\ \square\ \square \\ +\ \ \ \ \square\ \square \\ \hline 3\ 3\ 5\ 6 \end{array}$$

11.

?

216   91   173

The total is _____.

12.

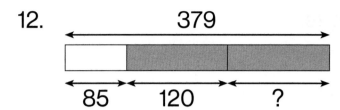

The value of the missing part is _____.

13.

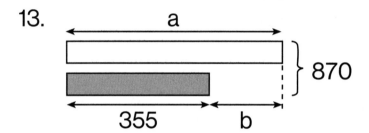

a) The value of the longer bar is _____.

b) The difference between the two bars is

_____.

14. Maria played a computer game.
    What was her final score at the end of the game?

Starting Score	Points Earned	Points Lost	Final Score
2,370	890	1,560	?

    Her final score was _____ points.

15. Andy wrote a number on a tag.
    It has the digits 0, 5, 6 and 8.
    It is the smallest number between 3,000 and 7,000.
    What number is it?

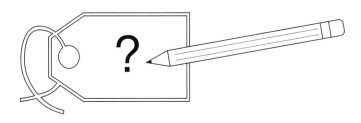

Section C (4 points each)

16. In one day, a total of 2,680 children visited a zoo.
1,450 of them were boys.
How many more boys than girls visited the zoo
that day?

_____ more boys than girls visited the zoo
on that day.

17. Bobbi, Daniel, and Arthur shared 2,000 trading cards.
Bobbi got 580 trading cards and Daniel got 316 more
than Bobbi.
How many trading cards did Arthur get?

Arthur got _____ trading cards.

18. Shop A has 1,298 more T-shirts than Shop B. If 365 T-shirts are transferred from Shop A to Shop B, how many more T-shirts will Shop A have than Shop B?

Shop A will have _____ more T-shirts than Shop B.

19. Akira put 5,893 beads in boxes A, B and C.
Box A and Box B contained a total of 2,750 beads.
Box B and Box C contained a total of 4,930 beads.
How many beads were there in each box?

Box A [ ]

Box B [ ]

Box C [ ]

20.

= 1,000

= 766

What is ?

```
┌─────────────────────────────┐
│                             │
│                             │
└─────────────────────────────┘
```

BLANK

Name: _____ Date: _____

Test A

55 min

Continual Assessment 1

Section A (2 points each)
Circle the correct option: **A**, **B**, **C**, or **D**.

1. In 4,783, the digit ___?___ is in the hundreds place.

    A 8   **B** 7

    C 3   **D** 4

2. Which of the following is <u>not</u> correct?

    A $3,765 = 3,000 + 700 + 60 + 5$

    B $7,036 = 7,000 + 30 + 6$

    C $4,023 = 4,000 + 200 + 3$

    D $6,904 = 6,000 + 900 + 4$

3. What is the missing number in the number pattern?

A 904   **B** 907

C 909   **D** 910

4. Which number completes the equation?

$8{,}000 + 74 + \boxed{?} = 8{,}074$

A 0   **B** 8

C 7   **D** 4

5. 10 hundreds less than __?__ is 1,800.

A 800   **B** 1,700

C 1,900   **D** 2,800

6. What is the smallest number that can be formed with the given digits?

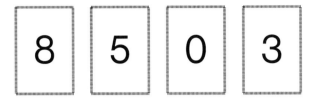

    A 3,058   **B** 3,085

    C 3,580   **D** 3,805

7. What is the missing number?

$$4{,}000 + 100 + 8 = 4{,}128 - \boxed{?}$$

    A 20   **B** 2

    C 200   **D** 2,000

8. The sum of 645 and __?__ is 1,000.

    A 355   **B** 455

    C 465   **D** 1,645

9. The missing digits in both boxes are the same.
   What is the digit?

$$2\boxed{?}09$$
$$+\ 1\ 3\ 4\ \boxed{?}$$
$$\overline{\ \ 4\ 2\ 5\ 8\ }$$

   A 1   **B** 5

   C 3   **D** 9

10. When Jean subtracted 4,132 from 6,825, she got
    2,793 as the answer.
    She made a mistake in the ___?___ place.

    A ones   **B** tens

    C hundreds   **D** thousands

Section B (2 points each)

11. Write the number four thousand, nine hundred fifty.

12. Write 7,344 in words.

13. What number is missing?

$$5{,}609 = 5{,}000 + \boxed{} + 9$$

14. Arrange the numbers in order.
    Begin with the greatest.

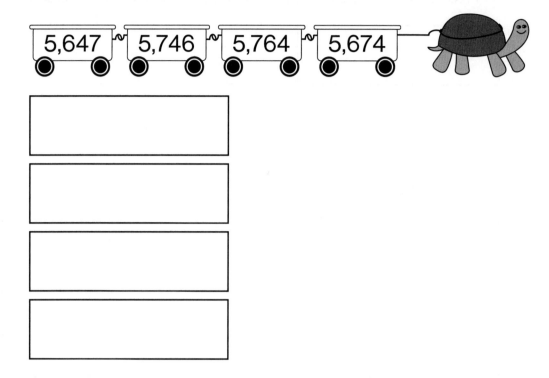

5,647 5,746 5,764 5,674

```
┌─────────────────────┐
│                     │
└─────────────────────┘
┌─────────────────────┐
│                     │
└─────────────────────┘
┌─────────────────────┐
│                     │
└─────────────────────┘
┌─────────────────────┐
│                     │
└─────────────────────┘
```

15. 1,000 more than 5,047 is _____.

16. 100 less than 2,000 is _____.

17.

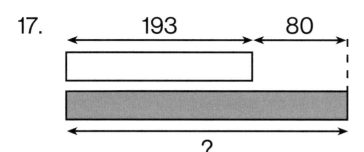

The value of the longer bar is _____.

18. Alice has 144 crayons.
Mason gives her another 88 crayons.
How many crayons does Alice have now?

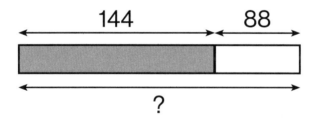

Alice has _____ crayons now.

19. 528 books in a library were checked out.
    There were 4,210 books left.
    How many books were there in the library at first?

20. Kane finished reading 248 pages of a book.
    He still had 155 pages to read.
    How many pages are there in the book altogether?

Section C (4 points each)

21. Joy has a total of 400 toy cars and toy airplanes. If she has 169 toy cars, how many <u>more</u> toy airplanes than toy cars does she have?

22. Joey saved $890.
He saved $360 more than his brother.
How much money did they save altogether?

23. Anna earned $1,000 from her yard sale.
She spent $320 on food, $250 on movies, and saved the rest.
How much did she save from her yard sale?

$ _____

24. In a competition, Team A and Team B completed a total of 3,200 sit-ups.
If Team A did 1,840 sit-ups, how many more sit-ups did Team A do than Team B?

Team A did _____ more sit-ups than Team B.

25. The difference between two numbers is 185.
If the greater number is 276, what is the sum of the
two numbers?

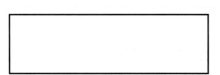

Extra Credit

1. $\star + \square + \bigcirc = 1{,}000$

   $\star + \square = 364$

   $\star + \bigcirc = 758$

   $\star = $ _____

2. The sum of two numbers is 50.
   The difference between the two numbers is 36.
   What are the two numbers?

Name: _____ Date: _____

Test B

55 min

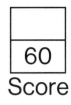

60

Score

Continual Assessment 1

Section A (2 points each)
Circle the correct option: **A**, **B**, **C**, or **D**.

1. The digit 7 in 7,053 stands for ___?___ .

    A 7   **B** 70

    C 700   **D** 7,000

2. In 5,432, which digit is in the hundreds place?

    A 5   **B** 2

    C 3   **D** 4

3. What is the missing number?
    $4{,}000 + \boxed{\ ?\ } + 50 + 6 = 4{,}856$

    A 8   **B** 80

    C 800   **D** 8,000

4. What number is shown in the box?

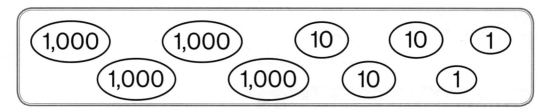

    A 4,032   **B** 4,230

    C 4,302   **D** 4,320

5. 100 less than 7,000 is ___?___ .

    A 7,010   **B** 7,100

    C 6,900   **D** 6,090

6. What is the missing number in the pattern?

    A 3,990   **B** 4,080

    C 4,800   **D** 4,980

7. What is the difference between 3,000 and 99?

      A 1,901   **B** 3,099

      C 2,911   **D** 2,901

8. The missing digits in both boxes are the same. What is the digit?

```
    3 6 ? 4
  + 2 ? 4 7
  ─────────
    6 2 0 1
```

      A 5   **B** 7

      C 6   **D** 4

9. What is the difference between the greatest and smallest number in this set?

7,924   3,897   7,938   7,893   3,982

   A 4,041   **B** 3,956

   C 3,996   **D** 3,911

10. If ▢ stands for the same digit, what is ▢?

$$\begin{array}{r} 2\ \square\ 0\ 6 \\ -\ 1\ 3\ 4\ \square \\ \hline 1\ 4\ 5\ 8 \end{array}$$

   A 9   **B** 2

   C 7   **D** 8

Section B (2 points each)

11. Write the number five thousand, thirty-eight.

(blank box)

12. Write 9,743 in words.

(blank box)

13. Write the missing number.

$3{,}000 + \boxed{} + 80 = 3{,}085$

14. Arrange the numbers in order.
Begin with the smallest.

3,689,   3,986,   3,968,   3,698

| |
| |

| |
| |

| |
| |

| |
| |

15. What is the greatest 4-digit number that can be made using these digits?

2   5   0   9

| |
| |

16. Write the missing digit.

$$
\begin{array}{r}
2\ 3\ 7\ 5 \\
+\quad 6\ \square\ 9 \\
\hline
3\ 0\ 0\ 4
\end{array}
$$

17. Which two numbers below make 10,000?

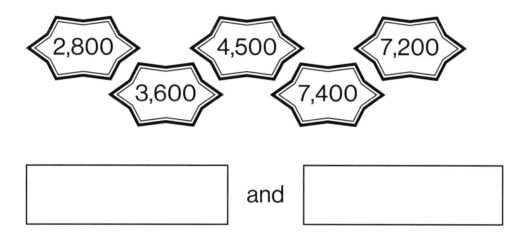

2,800   4,500   7,200

3,600   7,400

[   ] and [   ]

18. When Patel subtracted 3,321 from 4,813, he got 1,482 as the answer.

He made a mistake in the _____ place.

19. Juliet has 1,000 badges and Evelyn has 798 badges.
How many more badges does Juliet have than Evelyn?

20.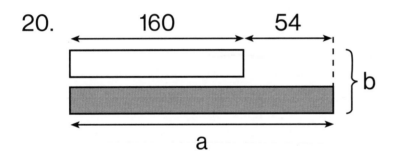

   a)   The value of the longer bar is _____.

   b)   The total of the two bars is _____.

Section C (4 points each)

21. Amara has $5 more than May.
    Harlan has $3 less than Amara.
    Who has the least money?

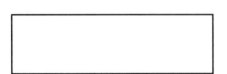

22. The difference between 2 numbers is 120.
    If the smaller number is 64, what is the sum of the
    2 numbers?

23. In a school, there are 1,860 students.
900 of them are girls and the rest are boys.
How many <u>more</u> boys than girls are there?

24. During a sale, 2,850 video games were sold on Saturday.
970 fewer video games were sold on Sunday.
How many video games were sold on both days?

25. Three boys were playing a computer game. John scored 1,520 points, Tomás scored 760 points more than John, and Colin scored 890 fewer points than Tomás.
What was their total score?

Their total score was _____.

Extra Credit

1. Look at the pattern below.
   How many circles will be in the 8th group?

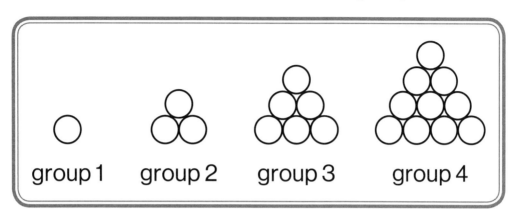

group 1   group 2   group 3   group 4

The 8th group will have _____ circles.

2. 🌰 and 🐿️ each stand for a number.

🌰 + 🐿️ = 48

🌰 − 🐿️ = 26

🌰 stands for _____.

🐿️ stands for _____.

Name: _____   Date: _____

Test A

45 min

50
Score

Unit 3 Multiplication and Division

Section A (2 points each)
Circle the correct option: **A**, **B**, **C**, or **D**.

1. Which of the following does not describe the number of apples correctly?

    A 4 × 6   **B** 6 × 6

    C 6 + 6 + 6 + 6   **D** 4 + 4 + 4 + 4 + 4 + 4

2. What number is missing?

$$\boxed{\ ?\ } \times 3 = (5 \times 3) + (4 \times 3)$$

    A 5   **B** 1

    C 9   **D** 10

3. Fill in the blank.

$4 \times 3 = 8$ | ? | 4

A $\times$ **B** $+$

C $-$ **D** $\div$

4. What is the missing number?

1	?	7	10
3	12	21	30

A 5   **B** 6

C 3   **D** 4

5. A pack of 4 batteries cost $3.
   How much did Ali pay for 20 batteries?

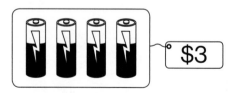

A $5   **B** $8

C $12   **D** $15

Section B (2 points each)

6. Write two number equations for the picture below.

$$\boxed{} \times \boxed{} = \boxed{}$$

$$\boxed{} \div \boxed{} = \boxed{}$$

7. Put 20 crackers into stacks of 3.

   a) How many stacks of crackers are there?

   b) How many crackers are left?

8. Multiply.

$$
\begin{array}{r}
2\ 0\ 6 \\
\times\quad\ \ 3 \\
\hline
\\
\hline
\end{array}
$$

9. Divide.

$$
4\overline{)4\ 2\ 8}
$$

```
┌─────────────────┐
│                 │
│                 │
└─────────────────┘
```

10. Cross out (x) all the even numbers.

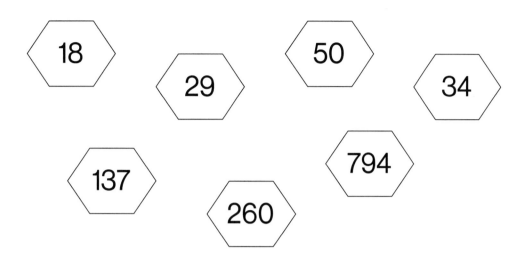

How many even numbers are there in all?

[ ]

11. Write >, <, or =.

3×7 ◯ 5×4

12. Peter bought the same number of sandwiches and drinks.
He paid a total of $20.
How many sandwiches did he buy?

sandwich
$4

drink
$1

He bought _____ sandwiches.

13. There are five Grade 3 classes in a school.
There are 24 students in each class.
How many Grade 3 students are there in the school?

14. There are 205 marbles in a bag.
How many marbles are there in 4 bags?

15. A stapler costs $5.
Renee has $32.
How many staplers can she buy?

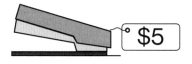

Section C (4 points each)

16. Jamal bought headphones and a tablet.
The headphones cost $38.
The tablet cost 4 times as much as the headphones.

a) How much did the tablet cost?

The tablet cost _____.

b) How much did Jamal pay altogether?

Jamal paid _____ altogether.

17. In a food drive, Adrianna collected 312 cans of food. She collected 3 times as many cans of food as Terry.

   a)   How many cans of food did Terry collect?

   Terry collected _____ cans of food.

   b)   How many more cans of food did Adrianna collect than Terry?

   Adrianna collected _____ more cans of food than Terry.

18. There are 200 coins in Sam's collection.
    He has 4 times as many foreign coins as local coins.

    a) How many local coins does he have?

    He has _____ local coins.

    b) How many foreign coins does he have?

    He has _____ foreign coins.

19. Jessie had $50.
    After buying 4 art sets, she had $26 left.
    How much did each art set cost?

    Each art set cost _____.

20. Diana folded 104 paper planes.
She folded 4 times as many paper planes as her brother.
How many more paper planes did Diana fold than her brother?

Diana folded _____ more paper planes than her brother.

Name: _____ Date: _____

Test B

45 min

50
Score

Unit 3 Multiplication and Division

Section A (2 points each)
Circle the correct option: **A**, **B**, **C**, or **D**.

1. What is the missing sign?

    $6 + 6 + 12 = 4 \, (?) \, 6$

    A +   **B** −

    C ×   **D** ÷

2. 6×9 is ___?___ more than 6×7.

    A 6×1 **B** 6×2

    C 6×3 **D** 6×4

3. How many odd numbers are there below?

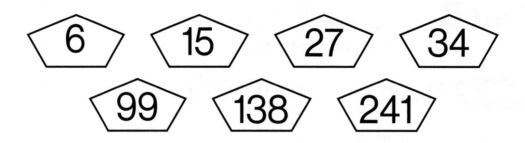

    A 5   **B** 7

    C 3   **D** 4

4. Look at the pattern.
   What number is K?

7	8	9	...	167
35	40	45	...	K

    A 880   **B** 835

    C 172   **D** 162

5.  stands for a number.

 What number is 🐸 ?

A 6

B 5

C 3

D 4

Section B (2 points each)

6. How many 4s are there in 32?

[ ]

7. Write the missing number.

$$8 + 8 + 8 + \boxed{} = 5 \times 8$$

8. Multiply.

$$
\begin{array}{r}
2\ 3\ 6 \\
\times\quad\ \ 3 \\
\hline
 \\
\hline
\end{array}
$$

9. Divide.

$$2 \overline{)3\ 7\ 9}$$

10. Write the missing number.

$$104 \times 4 = 400 + \boxed{} + 6$$

11. Look at the numbers on the cards below.
    Find the greatest value by multiplying two of the
    numbers together and then adding the third number.

8   5   7

$$\boxed{}$$

12. Mr. and Mrs. Lim took their 3 children to a zoo.

Admission Ticket	
Adult	$10
Child	$6

How much did they pay for their tickets?

They paid _____ for their tickets.

13. The product of two numbers is 110.
If one of the numbers is 5, the other number

is _____.

14. A bag of 4 oranges costs $3.
Eileen wants to buy 20 oranges.
How much will she have to pay?

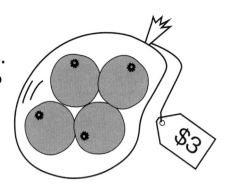

She will have to pay _____.

15. Each ☆ and ✦ stands for a number.

☆ + ☆ + ☆ = 12

☆ × ✦ = 24

✦ + ✦ + ✦ = ⬜

Section C (4 points each)

16. 🐠 + 🦀 🦀 🦀 🦀 = 1,400

    🐠 + 🦀 = 473

    🦀 = _____

17. Look at the diagram below.
    What is the missing sum?

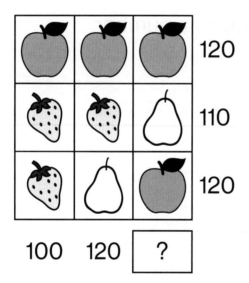

100   120 | ? |

18. There were 6 erasers in a package.
    Ms. Sanders bought 3 packages for her students.
    If each student got 2 erasers, how many students
    were there?

    There were _____ students.

19. The sum of three numbers is 168.
    The 2nd number is twice the 1st number.
    The 3rd number is 3 times the 1st number.
    What is the 3rd number?

    The 3rd number is _____.

20. Mr. James bought 150 balloons.
    If he had 6 more balloons, he could give each student in his class 4 balloons.
    How many students are there in his class?

    There are _____ students in his class.

Name: _____ Date: _____

Test A  45 min

□
50
Score

Unit 4 Multiplication Tables of 6, 7, 8, and 9

Section A (2 points each)
Circle the correct option: **A**, **B**, **C**, or **D**.

1. 9 girls shared 72 buttons equally.
   How many buttons did each girl get?

   A 63   **B** 9

   C 8   **D** 7

2. 6 balloons cost $9.
   Thomas bought 54 balloons
   for a party.
   How much did he pay?

   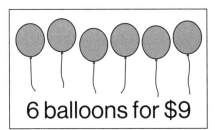
   6 balloons for $9

   A $6   **B** $36

   C $54   **D** $81

3. Multiply.

$$
\begin{array}{r}
5\ 0\ 4 \\
\times\qquad 9 \\
\hline
\\
\hline
\end{array}
$$

  A 4,506   **B** 4,536

  C 4,596   **D** 486

4. Look at the pattern.
    What is the value of M?

3	4	5	...	201
27	36	45	...	M

  A 188   **B** 210

  C 809   **D** 1,809

5. Divide.

$$6\,)\overline{3\ 0\ 6}$$

  A 51   **B** 56

  C 501   **D** 151

Section B (2 points each)

6. Write the missing number.

$$5 \times \boxed{} = 6 + 6 + 6 + 6 + 6$$

7. Look at the pattern.
   Write the missing number.

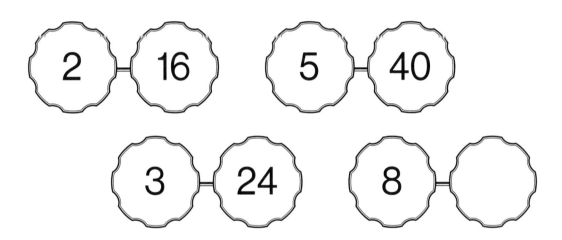

8. Write the missing numbers.

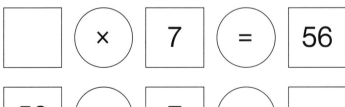

$$\boxed{} \times 7 = 56$$

$$56 \div 7 = \boxed{}$$

9. Tina used 6 straws to make a house as shown below. How many such houses can she make with 126 straws?

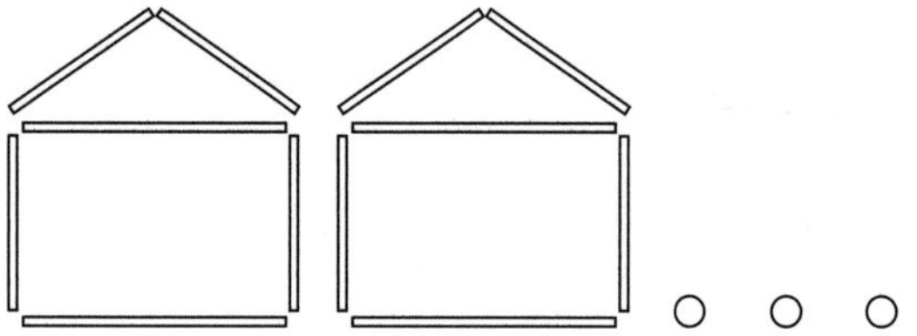

10. If  stands for 54 flowers,

how many flowers do  stand for?

11. There are 4 AA batteries and 2 AAA batteries in a packet.
Sari bought 7 packets of batteries.
How many batteries did she buy in total?

12. There are 808 seats in an auditorium.
The seats are arranged in 8 rows.
How many seats are there in each row?

13. At a party, each child was given 3 blue balloons, 3 yellow balloons, and 2 red balloons.
How many balloons were given out if 105 children attended the party?

14. When two of the numbers below are multiplied together, the product cannot be divided by 2 exactly.
What are the two numbers?

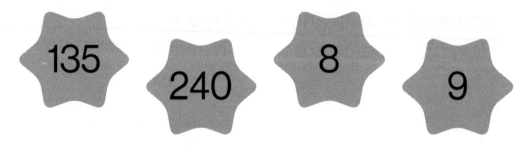

135   240   8   9

15. I am a 2-digit even number.
    I am greater than 60 but smaller than 100.
    When you multiply my ones digit with my tens digit,
    the product is 18.
    What number am I?


```
┌─────────────────────────┐
│                         │
│                         │
└─────────────────────────┘
```

Section C (4 points each)

16. A store owner bought 352 pens.
    She kept them in boxes in the storeroom.
    If each box could only store a maximum of 7 pens,
    what was the least number of boxes she would need?

    The least number of boxes needed is _____.

17. Nelson could buy 8 comic books for $56.
    Nelson has $63.
    How many comic books can he buy?

    He can buy _____ comic books.

18. 42 students in a class were seated in groups of 6. Each group donated 10 cans of food to the canned food drive.
How many cans of food did the class donate in all?

The class donated _____ cans of food in all.

19. Mr. Lovell wants to buy 32 journals for his students. How much will he have to pay if the journals are sold at 4 for $9?

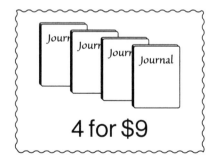

4 for $9

He will have to pay _____.

20. Given that 🏈 + ⚽ = 14,

and 🏈 + ⚽ + 🏈 = 20,

what is 🏈 × ⚽ ?

Name: _____   Date: _____

Test B

45 min

50
Score

Unit 4 Multiplication Tables of 6, 7, 8, and 9

Section A (2 points each)
Circle the correct option: **A**, **B**, **C**, or **D**.

1. What is the missing digit?

$$
\begin{array}{r}
9\ \boxed{?}\ 6 \\
\times\ \quad\ 7 \\
\hline
6\ 4\ 1\ 2 \\
\hline
\end{array}
$$

A 1   **B** 2

C 3   **D** 4

2. Which of the following will not have a remainder?

A $94 \div 3$ **B** $125 \div 4$

C $315 \div 7$ **D** $266 \div 6$

3. What is the missing number?

   $\boxed{\ ?\ } \div 8 = 14\,R\,6$

   A 68   **B** 62

   C 112   **D** 118

4. 105 beads are needed to make 1 necklace.
   How many beads are needed to make 7 necklaces?

   A 735   **B** 7,035

   C 105   **D** 15

5. Look at the pattern.
   Which shape is in the 50th position?

   1st   5th   9th

   A ■   **B** ▲

   C ●   **D** ☆

Section B (2 points each)

6.  ◯ stands for a number.
    If ◯ × ◯ = 49, what is ◯ ?

    ```
    ┌─────────────────────┐
    │                     │
    │                     │
    │                     │
    └─────────────────────┘
    ```

7. Write the missing number.

    $38 \times 7 = 30 \times 7 +$ ┌─────────────┐
                                 │   │
                                 └─────────────┘

8. Write the missing number.

    (2)—(14)   (4)—(28)

        (3)—(21)   (◯)—(357)

9. Which of the following gives the greatest value?

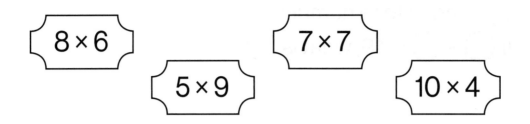

8 × 6

5 × 9

7 × 7

10 × 4

10. Look at the number patterns.
    Which set does the number 81 belong to?

Set A
6, 12, 18, 24, ...

Set B
7, 14, 21, 28, ...

Set C
8, 16, 24, 32 ...

Set D
9, 18, 27, 36 ...

11. Jasmine has 10 blue markers and 4 <u>more</u> red markers than blue markers.
If she wants to pack 6 markers in a bag, how many bags does she need?

┌─────────────────────┐
│   │
│   │
└─────────────────────┘

12. There are 6 squares and 3 triangles.
Paco draws 4 dots inside each square and 5 dots inside each triangle.
How many dots does Paco draw altogether?

□ □ □ □ □ □

△ △ △

┌─────────────────────┐
│   │
│   │
└─────────────────────┘

13. A worker was paid $768 for working 6 days.
    If she worked 8 hours a day, how much was she paid
    an hour?

    She was paid _____ an hour.

14. Write the missing number.

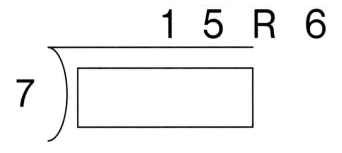

15.  = 36

 = 72

 = [   ]

Section C (4 points each)

16. A florist had 500 flowers in her shop.
    She gave 290 flowers to a hospital.
    Then she arranged the remaining flowers equally
    into bouquets of 7.

    a)   How many bouquets were there?

    There were _____ bouquets.

    b)   If each bouquet was sold at $9, how much
         money did she collect?

    She collected _____.

17. There are 144 pens in Box A.
     There are 6 times as many pens in Box B as in
     Box A.
     How many pens must be transferred from Box B
     to Box A so that there is an equal number of pens
     in each box?

     _____ pens must be tranferred.

18. Rupa packed 6 bagels into a box.
     After she had packed 29 boxes of bagels, she had
     3 bagels left.
     How many bagels were there altogether?

     There were _____ bagels altogether.

19. Parker has 301 marbles.
    He wants to divide the marbles equally among
    8 friends.
    He needs some more marbles so that each friend
    gets an equal number of marbles.
    What is the least number of additional marbles he
    will need?

    He will need at least _____ more marbles.

20. Fatima is making a pattern using square tiles as
    shown below.
    How many square tiles will she need to build the
    6th figure?

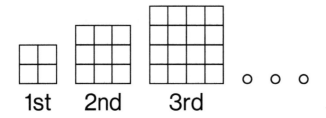

    1st   2nd   3rd

Name: _____ Date: _____

Test A 30 min

Length

┌──────┐
│   │
├──────┤
│ 30 │
└──────┘
Score

Section A (2 points each)
Circle the correct option: **A**, **B**, **C**, or **D**.

1. We add __?__ to get 1 m.

    A 5 cm and 5 cm

    B 25 cm and 25 cm

    C 36 cm and 64 cm

    D 235 cm and 765 cm

2. 5,098 m = │ 5 │ km │ ? │ m

    A 89   **B** 98

    C 908   **D** 9

3. What is the distance from Delaney's house to the playground?

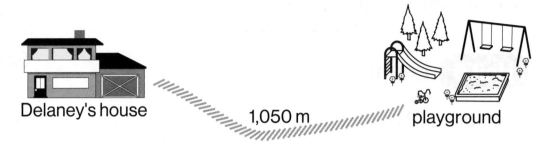

Delaney's house   1,050 m   playground

A 1 km 500 m   **B** 10 km 5 m

C 1 km 50 m   **D** 10 km 50 m

4. 22 inches = $\boxed{?}$ ft $\boxed{?}$ in.

A 2 yd 2 ft   **B** 2 ft 2 in.

C 1 ft 8 in.   **D** 1 ft 10 in.

5. Which one is the longest?

A 1 mi   **B** 2 yd

C 3 ft   **D** 4 in.

Section B (2 points each)

6. Circle the most likely distance between the bus stop near Zaey's house and the bus stop at her school.

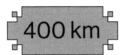 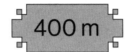 

400 km   400 m   400 cm

7. Which of the following lengths is the longest?

| 120 cm | 1 m 30 cm | 2 m | 90 cm |

[ ]

8. Write >, < or =.

6 yd 1 ft _____ 15 ft

9. What is the distance between the bus stop and the city library in km and m?

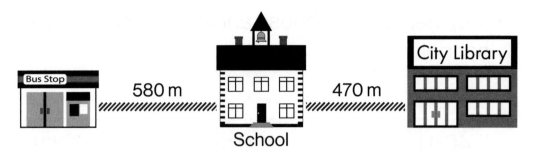

km	m

10. When Ferris stands on a 50-cm block, he is 17 cm taller than Grace.
   If Grace is 163 cm tall, how tall is Ferris?

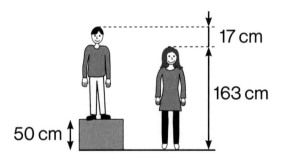

cm

11. A pole is 100 cm long.
    Selena paints 37 cm of it red,
    25 cm of it green and the rest blue.
    How many centimeters of the pole are painted blue?

    _____ of the pole are painted blue.

12. Mateo drove 3 km 150 m to the bank.
    He then drove 1 km 950 m to the post office.
    What is the total distance he drove?

    Mateo drove _____ km _____ m.

13. Alexis is 1 m 70 cm tall.
     She is 15 cm taller than Morgan.
     How tall is Morgan?

     Morgan is _____ m _____ cm tall.

14. A ribbon is 2 ft 5 in. long.
     What is its length in inches?

     The ribbon is _____ in.

15. A plant was 5 ft 10 in. tall.
    It grew 2 ft 10 in.
    How tall is the plant now?

The plant is _____ ft _____ in.
tall now.

BLANK

Name: _____ Date: _____

Test B  30 min

☐
30
Score

Unit 5 Length

Section A (2 points each)
Circle the correct option: **A, B, C,** or **D.**

1. A ribbon was cut into two pieces as shown below. What was the original length of the ribbon?

79 cm   125 cm

   A 2 m 4 cm

   B 2 m 40 cm

   C 20 m 4 cm

   D 20 m 40 cm

2. 5 ft – 7 in. is the same as __?__.

   A 4 ft 3 in.   **B** 4 ft 5 in.

   C 67 in.   **D** 57 in.

3. Which of the following is arranged in order from longest to shortest?

   A 1 yd, 24 in., 1 ft   **B** 5 ft, 12 in., 2 yd

   C 10 in., 10 ft, 10 yd   **D** 20 in., 2 ft, 1 yd

The table below shows the distances 4 children jogged over 2 days.
Use it to answer questions 4 and 5.

	Pedro	Sam	Jayla	Danny
Day 1	3 km 30 m	3 km 400 m	3,400 m	3 km 400 m
Day 2	3 km 40 m	4,000 m	4 km 400 m	4,040 m

4. Who jogged the shortest distance over the 2 days?

   A Pedro   **B** Sam

   C Jayla   **D** Danny

5. Who jogged the longest distance over the 2 days?

   A Pedro   **B** Sam

   C Jayla   **D** Danny

Section B (2 points each)

6. Circle the better estimate.

a) Length of a key

5 m   or   5 cm

b) Length of a swimming pool

50 m   or   50 cm

c) Height of a lamp pole

4 m   or   4 km

d) Distance between 2 towns

30 m   or   30 km

e) Length of an eraser

2 m   or   2 cm

f) Height of a table

80 m   or   80 cm

7. The length of a wire is 2 m 18 cm.
What is the length in cm?

cm

8. Use the map to complete the sentences.

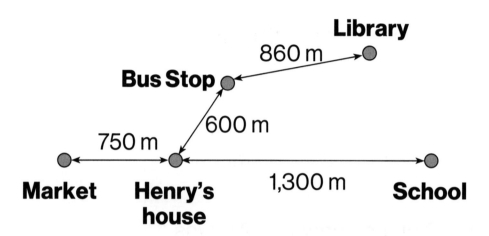

a) Henry's house is _____ km _____ m
from the library.

b) The school is _____ km _____ m
from the market.

9. Some poles are placed along a street at an equal distance of 3 m.
    If the length between the 1st and last poles is 114 m, how many poles are there?

    There are _____ poles.

10. A piece of rope 420 cm long is cut into 3 pieces: A, B, and C.
    B is 70 cm longer than C, but 40 cm shorter than A.
    What is the length of A?

11. Rowan has a jump rope that is 2 m 40 cm long.
Sydney has a jump rope that is 85 cm longer.
What is the total length of the two jump ropes?

The total length is _____ m _____ cm.

12. Nate jogged 1 km 200 m.
Eliza jogged 2,345 m.
How much farther did Eliza jog than Nate?

Eliza jogged _____ km _____ m
farther than Nate.

13. A baby dolphin is 3 ft 8 in. shorter than its mother.
    The mother dolphin is 7 ft 7 in. long.
    How long is the baby dolphin?

    The baby dolphin is _____ ft _____ in.
    long.

14. Abby has a ribbon 3 ft 3 in. long.
    Lily has a ribbon 2 yd long.
    Lucy has a ribbon 4 ft 11 in. long.
    Who has the longest ribbon?

    a)   _____ has the longest ribbon.

    b)   The longest ribbon is _____ ft _____ in.
          long.

15. A cloth was 2 yd 1 ft long.
Kiera made a scarf and 2 ft of cloth was left.
How much cloth did Kiera use to make the scarf?

Kiera used _____ yd _____ ft of
cloth to make the scarf.

Name: _____   Date: _____

Test A

55 min

```
     ┌─────┐
     │     │
     ├─────┤
     │ 60  │
     └─────┘
     Score
```

Continual Assessment 2

Section A (2 points each)
Circle the correct option: **A**, **B**, **C**, or **D**.

1. In 4,098, the digit 9 has the same value as __?__.

    A 9×1 **B** 9×10

    C 9×100 **D** $9 \times 1,000$

2. What is the missing number?

    $7,604 = 7,000 + \boxed{\ ?\ } + 4$

    A 6   **B** 60

    C 600   **D** 6,000

3. 6,789 is 1,000 less than __?__.

    A 5,789   **B** 6,889

    C 6,689   **D** 7,789

4. Which set of numbers are arranged from the smallest to the greatest?

    A 4,321,   4,312,   3,412,   2,143

    B 4,312,   4,321,   3,412,   2,143

    C 2,143,   3,412,   4,312,   4,321

    D 2,143,   3,412,   4,321,   4,312

5. Which of the following gives the smallest even number?

    A $3{,}000 + 900 + 80 + 4$

    B $3{,}000 + 800 + 40 + 9$

    C $3{,}000 + 800 + 90 + 4$

    D $3{,}000 + 400 + 80 + 9$

6. The missing number is ___?___.
$$4 + 4 + 4 + 4 + 4 = \boxed{?} \times 4$$

    A 20   **B** 5

    C 16   **D** 4

7. 7 days make up a week.
    42 days is how many weeks?

    A 6   **B** 7

    C 42   **D** 294

8. A toy snake is 1 m 9 cm long.
    How long is it in centimeters?

    A 19 cm   **B** 109 cm

    C 190 cm   **D** 1,009 cm

9. The total length of two pieces of wire is 17 m.
    If one piece is 3 m longer than the other, what is the
    length of the shorter piece?

    A 7 m   **B** 10 m

    C 14 m   **D** 20 m

10. What is 1 yd + 2 ft 11 in.?

    A 3 ft 11 in.   **B** 3 yd 11 in.

    C 5 ft 11 in.   **D** 5 ft

Section B (2 points each)

11. Write 8,457 in words.

```

```

12. Write the missing number.

$$3,000 + 70 + 5 = \boxed{}$$

13. Complete the number pattern.

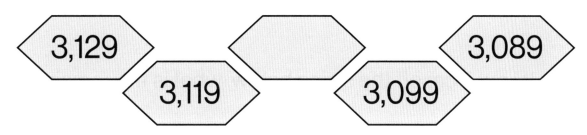

3,129   3,119   [ ]   3,099   3,089

14. Helen ties 102 sticks into bundles of 5.
    How many sticks are left over?

    _____ sticks are left over.

15. Write the missing digit.

$$
\begin{array}{r}
3\ 9\ 5\ 1 \\
+\ 2\ 1\ 1\ 0 \\
\hline
\boxed{}\ 0\ 6\ 1 \\
\hline
\end{array}
$$

16. José baked 39 fruit pies and 3 times as many chocolate pies.
How many pies did he bake altogether?

17. If I cut 7 cm off the string below, what is the remaining length?

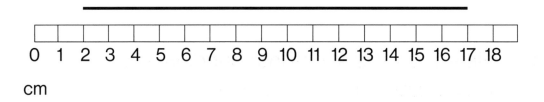

0 1 2 3 4 5 6 7 8 9 10 11 12 13 14 15 16 17 18

cm

18. Jude is 1 m tall.
He is 27 cm taller than his sister.
How tall is his sister?

```
┌─────────────────────────┐
│                         │
│                         │
└─────────────────────────┘
```

19. Adrien is 5 ft 5 in. tall.
Nia is 4 ft 9 in. tall.
How much taller is Adrien than Nia?

Adrien is _____ in. taller.

20. How many yards does 6 ft 6 in. and 2 ft 6 in. make?

_____ yd

Section C (4 points each)

21. Marin and Raj have a total of 37 T-shirts.
    Marin has 15 more T-shirts than Raj.
    How many T-shirts does Raj have?

    ┌─────────────────────┐
    │   │
    │   │
    └─────────────────────┘

22. A factory produces 1,250 cars in May and 380 <u>more</u> cars in June than in May.
    How many cars does the factory produce in the two months?

    ┌─────────────────────┐
    │   │
    │   │
    └─────────────────────┘

23. Jana has 150 charms for her charm bracelet.
She has three times as many as Maya.
How many charms do they have altogether?

```
┌──────────────────────┐
│                      │
│                      │
└──────────────────────┘
```

24. Ms. Patel bought 100 oranges.
After she gave 48 oranges to her students, she
packed the rest into bags of 5.
How many oranges were left unpacked?

_____ oranges were left unpacked.

25. The total length of strings A, B, and C is 57 m.
String A is 8 m longer than string B.
String C is 5 m shorter than string B.
What is the length of string A?

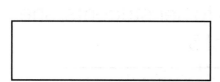

Extra Credit

1. Use the 4 digits to find the smallest product.

$$\begin{array}{r} \square\,\square\,\square \\ \times \qquad \square \\ \hline \\ \hline \end{array}$$

2.  = 1,000

▲ + ■ = 375

■ = _____

▲ = _____

BLANK

Name: _____ Date: _____

Test B  55 min

Continual Assessment 2

Section A (2 points each)
Circle the correct option: **A**, **B**, **C**, or **D**.

1.   6,093 is the same as ___?___.

    A 6 + 90 + 3,000

    B 6,000 + 90 + 3

    C 6,000 + 900 + 3

    D 6,000 + 9 + 30

2.   Which set of numbers is arranged from smallest to greatest?

    A 287,   278,   298,   308

    B 304,   340,   3,004,   3,040

    C 2,018,   2,180,   2,108,   2,810

    D 3,196,   3,096,   2,996,   2,986

3. Which of the following has the smallest value?

    A $50 - 10$ **B** $50 + 10$

    C 50×10 **D** $50 \div 10$

4. 4×5 is the same as ___?___ .

    A $4 + 4 + 4 + 4$ **B** $4 \times 4 \times 4 \times 4$

    C $5 + 5 + 5 + 5$ **D** $5 \times 5 \times 5 \times 5$

5. What is the missing number?

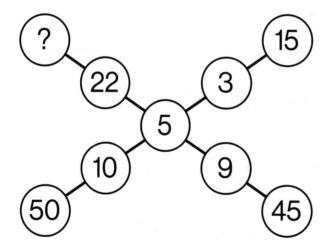

    A 100   **B** 110

    C 27   **D** 17

6. Which of the following is incorrect?

 A $88 \times 2 = 166$

 B $3 \times 63 = 180 + 9$

 C $162 \times 5 = 5 \times 162$

 D $164 \times 4 = 164 + 164 + 164 + 164$

7. What is the missing sign?
 $9 \times 8 = 144 \boxed{?} 2$

 A $+$ **B** $-$

 C $\times$ **D** $\div$

8. 2 km 70 m is the same as ___?___.

 A 207 m   **B** 270 m

 C 2,070 m   **D** 2,700 m

9. The height of a cabinet in the classroom is about ___?___ .

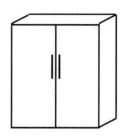

   A 18 km   **B** 18 m

   C 180 cm   **D** 18 cm

10. Which statement is not correct?

   A 1 in. is shorter than 1 ft but longer than 1 yd

   B 1 ft is longer than 1 in. but shorter than 1 yd

   C 1 mi is longer than 1,000 ft

   D 1 yd is longer than 1 in. but shorter than 1 mi

Section B (2 points each)

11. Write the number five thousand, seventy.

    ┌─────────────┐
    │   │
    │   │
    └─────────────┘

12. Arrange the numbers from greatest to smallest.

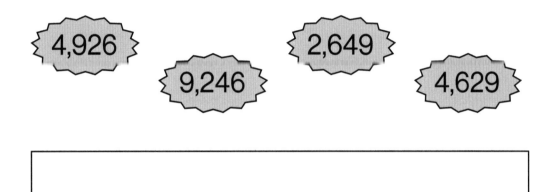

    ┌───┐
    │   │
    │   │
    │   │
    └───┘

13. Write the missing digit.

$$
\begin{array}{r}
5\ 8\ 6\ 7 \\
+\ 3\ \square\ 9\ 7 \\
\hline
9\ 8\ 6\ 4
\end{array}
$$

14. **A** stands for _____.

$$
\begin{array}{r}
7\ \mathbf{A}\ 6\ 5 \\
-\ 2\ 3\ 9\ 7 \\
\hline
5\ 5\ 6\ 8
\end{array}
$$

15. A box contains 14 bananas.
    How many bananas are there in 5 boxes?

```
┌─────────────────┐
│                 │
│                 │
└─────────────────┘
```

16. Anya puts 167 flowers into bundles of 5.
    How many flowers are left over?

```
┌─────────────────┐
│                 │
│                 │
└─────────────────┘
```

17. Write the missing number.

$9 \times 125 = 9 \times 100 +$ ⬚

18. Ali lives 2 km 40 m from his school.
    What is the distance in meters?

    ┌─────────────────────┐
    │   m │
    └─────────────────────┘

19. The total length of 7 train cars is 91 m.
    What is the length of each train car?

    ┌─────────────────────┐
    │   m │
    └─────────────────────┘

20. A ribbon is 2 ft long.
    Is the total length of 9 ribbons greater than 5 yd?
    Circle the correct answer.

    YES   NO

Section C (4 points each)

21. In a double-decker bus, there are 26 more people in the lower deck than in the upper deck.
12 people move from the lower deck to the upper deck.
How many <u>more</u> people are in the lower deck now?

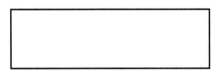

22. A farmer had 1,000 eggs.
After she sold 670 eggs, she kept the rest in boxes of 6.
How many boxes of eggs were there?

23. Teo paid $75 for 2 books and a magazine.
    If each book cost twice as much as the magazine,
    what was the cost of each book?

24. I am a number. When I am multiplied by myself,
    then added to 11, the answer is 60.
    What number am I?

25. 18 plants are planted along a street.
    The distance between every two plants is 3 m.
    What is the distance between the first and the last
    plants?

    m

Tests 3A

Extra Credit

1. X stands for _____.

$$4 \overline{) 6 \; X \; X} \quad {\large 1 \; 5 \; X}$$

2. Avery has as many rubber bands as D'Shon.

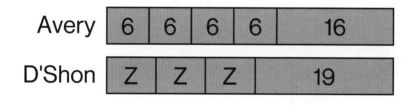

Avery	6	6	6	6	16

| D'Shon | Z | Z | Z | 19 |

Z stands for _____ rubber bands.

Answer Key and Detailed Solutions

Unit 1 | **Test A**

1. C
2. D
3. C
4. D
5. B
6a. 4,209
6b. 8,088
7a. seven thousand, nineteen
7b. five thousand, three hundred forty
8a. thousands
8b. 200
9. 2,099
10. 8,710
11. 5,141
12. 5,658
13.

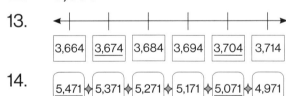

14.

15a. 4,600
15b. 5,000

Unit 1 | **Test B**

1. C
2. B
3. D
4. C
5. D
6. 3,406, 4,036, 6,340, 6,430
7. 1,999
8. 4
9. 1,368
10. 7,405
11. Thousands digit = 2
    Tens digit = 6 + 3 = 9
    Ones digit = 9 − 4 = 5
    Hundreds digit = 0
    Answer: 2,095
12. A and E
13. Pattern: The thousands digit and ones digit remain the same. The hundreds digit increases by 1. The tens digit increases by 2.
    Answer: 1,980
14. FALSE
15a. 1,000
15b. 900

1. A

2. B

3. B

4. A

5. C

6. $3{,}122 + 1{,}434 = 4{,}556$

7. $2{,}789 - 620 = 2{,}169$

8.
$$
\begin{array}{r}
2\ 0\ 1\ \boxed{4} \\
+\ 5\ 3\ \boxed{5}\ 4 \\
\hline
7\ 3\ 6\ 8
\end{array}
$$

9.
$$
\begin{array}{r}
4\ 7\ 9\ \boxed{6} \\
-\ \ \ 5\ \boxed{4}\ 3 \\
\hline
4\ 2\ 5\ 3
\end{array}
$$

10. $412 - 276 = 136$

11. $850 - 566 = 284$

12a. $336 - 98 = 238$

12b. $336 + 238 = 574$

13. $1{,}466 + 230 = 1{,}696$
1,696 stickers

14. $5{,}775 - 430 = 5{,}345$
5,345 skateboards

15. $4{,}138 - 1{,}230 = 2{,}908$
2,908 meatballs

16a. $1{,}964 - 350 = 1{,}614$
He collected 1,614 cards.

16b. $1{,}964 + 1{,}614 = 3{,}578$
Both of them collected 3,578 cards together.

17. $4{,}080 + 1{,}122 = 5{,}202$
$5{,}202 + 4{,}080 = 9{,}282$
There are 9,282 books altogether in the library.

18. $530 + 1{,}700 = 2{,}230$ (greater)
$2{,}230 + 530 = 2{,}760$
The sum of the two numbers is 2,760.

19. $457 - 120 = 337$ (Brian)
$1{,}045 - 457 - 337 = 251$
Connie collected 251 used books.

20. $2{,}850 - 1{,}730 = 1{,}120$

1. C

2. A

3. D

4. C

5. D

6. $4{,}000 - 70 = 3{,}930$

7. $5{,}470 - 2{,}398 = 3{,}072$
$3{,}072 = 3{,}000 + 70 + 2$
Answer: 3,000

8. $3{,}000 - 1{,}370 = 1{,}630$
$1{,}370 + 1{,}694 = 3{,}064$

	3,000	3,064	
	1,630	1,370	1,694
954	676	694	1,000

9.
```
    5 0 0 2
  -[3]3 7 8
    1 6 2 4
```

10. Accept all reasonable answers. For example,
```
    3 2[8][9]        3 2[6][7]
  +    [6][7]  or  +    [8][9]
    3 3 5 6          3 3 5 6
```

11. $216 + 91 + 173 = 480$

12. $379 - 85 - 120 = 174$

13a. $870 - 355 = 515$

13b. $515 - 355 = 160$

14. $2{,}370 + 890 - 1{,}560 = 1{,}700$
Her final score was 1,700 points.

15. 5,068

16. $2{,}680 - 1{,}450 = 1{,}230$ (girls)
$1{,}450 - 1{,}230 = 220$
220 more boys than girls visited the zoo on that day.

17. $580 + 316 = 896$ (Daniel)
$2{,}000 - 580 - 896 = 524$ (Arthur)
Arthur got 524 trading cards.

18. $1{,}298 - 365 - 365 = 568$
Shop A will have 568 more T-shirts than Shop B.

19. $2{,}750 + 4{,}930 = 7{,}680$
$7{,}680 - 5{,}893 = 1{,}787$ (B)
$2{,}750 - 1{,}787 = 963$ (A)
$4{,}930 - 1{,}787 = 3{,}143$ (C)
There were 963 beads in Box A, 1,787 beads in Box B, and 3,143 beads in Box C.

20. ▢ $= 1{,}000 - 766 = 234$

▬ $= 766 - 234 = 532$
$234 + 532 + 532 = 1{,}298$

1. B

2. C

3. A

4. A

5. D

6. A

7. A

8. A

9. D

10. C

11. 4,950

12. seven thousand, three hundred forty-four

13. 600

14. 5,764, 5,746, 5,674, 5,647

15. 6,047

16. 1,900

17. $193 + 80 = 273$

18. $144 + 88 = 232$
    Alice has 232 crayons now.

19. $528 + 4,210 = 4,738$
    4,738 books

20. $248 + 155 = 403$

21. $400 - 169 = 231$ (toy airplanes)
    $231 - 169 = 62$

22. $890 - $360 = $530 (brother)
    $890 + $530 = $1,420 (total)

23. $1,000 - $320 - $250 = $430

24. $3,200 - 1,840 = 1,360$ (B)
    $1,840 - 1,360 = 480$
    Team A did 480 more sit-ups than Team B.

25. $276 - 185 = 91$ (smaller number)
    $276 + 91 = 367$ (sum)

Extra Credit

1. $364 + 758 - 1,000 = 122$

2.

$50 - 36 = 14$
$14 \div 2 = 7$ (smaller number)
$36 + 7 = 43$ (greater number)

1. D

2. D

3. C

4. A

5. C

6. B

7. D

8. A

9. A

10. D

11. 5,038

12. nine thousand, seven hundred forty-three

13. 5

14. 3,689, 3,698, 3,968, 3,986

15. 9,520

16. 2

17. 2,800, 7,200

18. $4,813 - 3,321 = 1,492$
tens

19. $1,000 - 798 = 202$

20a. $160 + 54 = 214$

20b. $160 + 214 = 374$

21. May

22. $120 + 64 = 184$ (greater number)
$184 + 64 = 248$ (sum)

23. $1,860 - 900 = 960$ (boys)
$960 - 900 = 60$

24. $2,850 - 970 = 1,880$ (Sunday)
$2,850 + 1,880 = 4,730$

25. $1,520 + 760 = 2,280$ (Tomás)
$2,280 - 890 = 1,390$ (Colin)
$1,520 + 2,280 + 1,390 = 5,190$
Their total score was 5,190.

Extra Credit

1. 36

2. $48 - 26 = 22$

$22 \div 2 = 11$

$48 - 11 = 37$

1. B
2. C
3. B
4. D
5. D
6.

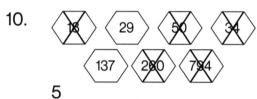

$$9 \times 4 = 36$$
$$36 \div 9 = 4$$

7a. 6 stacks
7b. 2 crackers
8. 618
9. 107
10.

18   29   50   34

137   280   794

5

11. >
12. $4 + $1 = $5
$20 ÷ $5 = 4
He bought 4 sandwiches.
13. 24 × 5 = 120 students
14. 4 × 205 = 820
820 marbles
15. 6 staplers × $5 = $30
7 staplers × $5 = $35
Answer: 6 staplers
16a. 4 × $38 = $152
The tablet cost $152.
16b. $152 + $38 = $190
Jamal paid $190 altogether.

17a. 312 ÷ 3 = 104
Terry collected 104 cans of food.
17b. 312 − 104 = 208
Adrianna collected 208 more cans of food than Terry.
18a. 200 ÷ 5 = 40
He has 40 local coins.
18b. 4 × 40 = 160
He has 160 foreign coins.
19. $50 − $26 = $24
$24 ÷ 4 = $6
Each art set cost $6.
20. 104 ÷ 4 = 26 (brother)
104 − 26 = 78
Diana folded 78 more paper planes than her brother.

Unit 3 — Test B

1. C
2. B
3. D
4. B
5. C
6. 8
7. 16
8. 708
9. 189 R 1
10. $104 \times 4 = 416$
    $416 = 400 + \underline{10} + 6$
    Answer: 10
11. $8 \times 7 = 56$
    $56 + 5 = 61$
    Answer: 61
12. $2 \times \$10 = \$20$
    $3 \times \$6 = \$18$
    $\$20 + \$18 = \$38$
    They paid $38 for their tickets.
13. $110 \div 5 = 22$
14. $20 \div 4 = 5$ bags
    $5 \times \$3 = \$15$
    She will have to pay $15.
15. $4 + 4 + 4 = 12$
    $4 \times 6 = 24$
    $6 + 6 + 6 = \underline{18}$
16. $1{,}400 - 473 = 927$
    $927 \div 3 = 309$
    Answer: 309

17. $= 120 \div 3 = 40$
    $100 - 40 = 60$

    $= 60 \div 2 = 30$

    $= 120 - 30 - 40 = 50$

    $40 + 40 + 50 = 130$
    Answer: 130
18. $6 \times 3 = 18$
    $18 \div 2 = 9$
    There were 9 students.
19.
    $168 \div 6 = 28$
    $3 \times 28 = 84$
    The 3rd number is 84.
20. $150 + 6 = 156$
    $156 \div 4 = 39$
    There are 39 students in his class.

1. C

2. D

3. B

4. D

5. A

6. 6

7. $2 \times 8 = 16$
   $5 \times 8 = 40$
   $3 \times 8 = 24$
   $8 \times 8 = 64$
   Answer: 64

8. | 8 | × | 7 | = | 56 |

   | 56 | ÷ | 7 | = | 8 |

9. $126 \div 6 = 21$
   21 houses

10. $54 \div 6 = 9$
    $5 \times 9 = 45$
    45 flowers

11. $4 + 2 = 6$
    $6 \times 7 = 42$
    Answer: 42 batteries

12. $808 \div 8 = 101$
    101 seats

13. $3 + 3 + 2 = 8$
    $105 \times 8 = 840$
    840 balloons

14. When 2 odd numbers are multiplied, the product will be an odd number. An odd number cannot be divided by 2 exactly.
    Answer: 135 and 9

15. The possible tens digit are: 6, 7, 8, and 9.
    $6 \times 3 = 18$
    $9 \times 2 = 18$
    So, the possible 2-digit numbers are: 63 and 92.
    63 is not an even number, so I am is 92.

16. $352 \div 7 = 50 \text{ R } 2$
    $50 + 1 = 51$
    The least number of boxes needed is 51.

17. $\$56 \div 8 = \$7$
    $\$63 \div \$7 = 9$
    He can buy 9 comic books.

18. $42 \div 6 = 7$
    $7 \times 10 = 70$
    The class donated 70 cans of food in all.

19. $32 \div 4 = 8$
    $8 \times \$9 = \$72$
    He will have to pay $72.

20. $20 - 14 = 6$
    $14 - 6 = 8$
    $6 \times 8 = 48$
    Answer: 48

1. A

2. C

3. D

4. A

5. B

6. 7

7. $8 \times 7 = 56$

8. $357 \div 7 = 51$

9. $8 \times 6 = 48$
   $7 \times 7 = 49$
   $5 \times 9 = 45$
   $10 \times 4 = 40$
   Answer: 7×7

10. Set A: count by 6s
    Set B: count by 7s
    Set C: count by 8s
    Set D: count by 9s
    Counting by 9s, we can get 81.
    Answer: Set D

11. $10 + 4 = 14$ (red)
    $10 + 14 = 24$ (total)
    $24 \div 6 = 4$

12. $6 \times 4 = 24$
    $3 \times 5 = 15$
    $24 + 15 = 39$

13. $\$768 \div 6 = \$128$
    $\$128 \div 8 = \$16$
    She was paid $16 an hour.

14. $15 \times 7 = 105$
    $105 + 6 = 111$

15. $9 + 9 + 9 + 9 = 36$
    So, 🐰 $= 9$
    $9 \times 8 = 72$
    So, 🦊 $= 8$

16a. $500 - 290 = 210$
    $210 \div 7 = 30$
    There were 30 bouquets.

16b. $30 \times \$9 = \$270$
    She collected $270.

17.   144
    A
    B
    $144 \times 5 = 720$
    $720 \div 2 = 360$
    360 pens must be transferred.

18. $29 \times 6 = 174$
    $174 + 3 = 177$
    There were 177 bagels altogether.

19. $301 \div 8 = 37 \text{ R } 5$
    $8 - 5 = 3$
    He will need at least 3 more marbles.

20. 1st: $2 \times 2 = 4$
    2nd: $3 \times 3 = 9$
    3rd: $4 \times 4 = 16$
    ...
    6th: $7 \times 7 = 49$
    Answer: 49 square tiles

Unit 5   Test A

1. C
2. B
3. C
4. D
5. A
6. 400 m
7. 2 m
8. >
9. 470 + 580 = 1,050 m
   1,050 m = 1 km 50 m
   Answer: 1 km 50 m
10. 163 + 17 − 50 = 130 cm
    Answer: 130 cm
11. 100 − 37 − 25 = 38
    38 cm of the pole are
    painted blue.
12. 5 km 100 m
13. 1 m 55 cm
14. 29 in.
15. 8 ft 8 in.

Unit 5   Test B

1. A
2. B
3. A
4. A
5. C
6a. 5 cm
6b. 50 m
6c. 4 m
6d. 30 km
6e. 2 cm
6f. 80 cm
7. 200 cm + 18 cm = 218 cm
8a. 600 m + 860 m
    = 1,460 m = 1 km 460 m
    Henry's house is 1 km 460 m
    from the library.
8b. 750 m + 1,300 m
    = 2,050 m = 2 km 50 m
    The school is 2 km 50 m
    from the market.
9. 114 ÷ 3 = 38 gaps
   38 + 1 = 39 poles
   There are 39 poles.
10.
    420 − 70 − 70 − 40 = 240 cm
    240 ÷ 3 = 80 cm
    80 + 70 + 40 = 190 cm
    The length of A is 190 cm.
11. 5 m 65 cm
12. 1 km 145 m
13. 3 ft 11 in.
14a. Lily
14b. 6 ft 0 in.
15. 1 yd 2 ft

1. B

2. C

3. D

4. C

5. C

6. B

7. A

8. B

9. A

10. C

11. eight thousand, four hundred fifty-seven

12. 3,075

13. 3,109

14. $102 \div 5 = 20$ R 2
2 sticks are left over.

15. 6

16. $39 \times 3 = 117$ (chocolate pies)
$39 + 117 = 156$ (total)

17. $15 - 7 = 8$ cm

18. $100 - 27 = 73$ cm

19. Adrien is 8 in. taller.

20. 3 yd.

21.
$37 - 15 = 22$
$22 \div 2 = 11$ (Raj)

22. $1,250 + 380 = 1,630$ (June)
$1,250 + 1,630 = 2,880$ (total)

23. $150 \div 3 = 50$ (Maya)
$150 + 50 = 200$ (total)

24. $100 - 48 = 52$
$52 \div 5 = 10$ R 2
2 oranges were left unpacked.

25.
$57 - 5 - 5 - 8 = 39$ m
$39 \div 3 = 13$ m (C)
$13 + 5 + 8 = 26$ m (A)

Extra Credit

1. $247 \times 1 = 247$

2. $1,000 - 375 - 375 = 250$ (■)
$375 - 250 = 125$ (▲)

Continual Assessment 2) Test B

1. B

2. B

3. D

4. C

5. B

6. A

7. D

8. C

9. C

10. A

11. 5,070

12. 9,246, 4,926, 4,629, 2,649

13. 9

14. 9

15. $5 \times 14 = 70$

16. $33 \times 5 = 165$
$167 - 165 = 2$

17. $9 \times 25 = 225$

18. 2,040 m

19. $91 \div 7 = 13$ m

20. 9×2 ft = 18 ft
5 yd = 15 ft
YES

21. $26 - 12 - 12 = 2$

22. $1,000 - 670 = 330$
$330 \div 6 = 55$

23.

$\$75 \div 5 = \$15$ (magazine)
$2 \times \$15 = \$30$ (book)

24. $60 - 11 = 49$
$7 \times 7 = 49$
So, I am 7.

25. $3 \times 17 = 51$ m

Extra Credit

1. $600 \div 4 = 150$
X stands for 0.

2. $4 \times 6 = 24$
$24 + 16 = 40$
$40 - 19 = 21$
$21 \div 3 = 7$